THE RAGGY DOLLS

WE ARE NOT AMUSED

FROM AN ORIGINAL IDEA BY
MELVYN JACOBSON

WRITTEN BY
NEIL INNES

ILLUSTRATED BY
STEVE SMALLMAN

YORKSHIRE
TELEVISION

BOXTREE LTD

THE RAGGY DOLLS

The Raggy Dolls live in the Reject Bin
in Mr Grimes's toy factory . . .

HI-FI was a talking doll, but when he was being tested, someone dropped him. He can still talk – but only with a stammer.

First published in Great Britain in 1990
By Boxtree Limited
Published in association with Yorkshire Television Limited

Text © Yorkshire Television 1990
Illustrations © Boxtree Limited 1990

The RAGGY DOLLS is a Trademark of Yorkshire Television Limited
© Melvyn Jacobson Productions Ltd

British Library Cataloguing in Publication Data
Innes, Neil
  We are not amused.
  I. Title   II. Smallman, Steve   III. Series
823.914 [J]

ISBN 1-85283-065-4

Designed by Bet Ayer
Edited by Cheryl Brown
Typeset by Tradespools Limited, Frome, Somerset
Origination by Culvergraphics
Printed in Great Britain by Richard Clays Ltd, Bungay, Suffolk

For Boxtree Limited
36 Tavistock Street, London WC2E 7PB

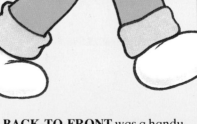

BACK-TO-FRONT was a handy man doll with a complete tool-kit, but somehow the machine put his head on the wrong way round.

LUCY was sewn together with faulty thread. Now her joints are so loose, she goes to pieces if she gets excited.

DOTTY was perfect in every way – until she got splashed with paint that would not come off.

CLAUDE is a French doll. There is nothing wrong with him. He was part of a special export order to France, but the machine made one too many – and he was left behind.

PRINCESS should have had a tiara, beautiful hair, and a splendid dress – but the machine went wrong, dressed her in rags and cropped her hair.

SAD SACK was a sample, but because he was nice and plump, he used up too much stuffing. This made him expensive, so nobody wanted him.

One afternoon, the Raggy Dolls were up the tree house playing 'I Spy', all except Hi-Fi who'd been busy in the tool shed all day.

"Hi spy with my little heye," said Princess, whose turn it was, ". . .something beginning with haitch!"

"No problem," said Back-to-Front, "its Heads." Princess shook her head.

"Hands?" said Dotty. Princess shook her head again.

"No, no," she said, "hit's Hi-Fi. Hand just wait everyone, he's carrying something! What his hit?"

It was a telescope. Hi-Fi proudly showed it to the others.

"I m-made it from c-cardboard tubes and a b-b-broken magnifying glass," he said.

"It's brilliant," said Dotty, "does it work?"

"I d-don't know," he stammered, "I've c-c-come up here to t-t-test it."

"Let's have a look," said Back-to-Front. Hi-Fi held the telescope for him. "Wow!" he exclaimed, "you can see for miles. . .Gosh!"

"What is it?" said Lucy.

Back-to-Front whistled in admiration.

"What can you see mon ami?" demanded Claude.

"There's somethin' goin' on over at Stoneybroke Hall," said Back-to-Front at last.

"Well, what is it?" said Dotty. "Come on, we're dying of suspense!"

"See for yourselves," said Back-to-Front, "I think it's an amusement park!"

Dotty looked through the eye-piece. She could see a big wheel, a helter-skelter, and the top of a merry-go-round.

"It is an amusement park," she gasped. "Come on, let's cut across the fields and see what's what!"

When they arrived at Stoneybroke Park, they could see the big wheel and all sorts of other amusements and rides.

They could hear lots of hammering and fixing going on.

"It isn't open to the p-p-public yet," said Hi-Fi.

"Let's take a closer look," said Dotty.

Creeping along the back of the stalls and tents, the Raggy Dolls suddenly came across a sort of train. It was parked on some rails that led into a dark doorway.

"It must be one of the rides," said Back-to-Front. "Come on, let's try it."

"I don't think we should," said Sad Sack.

"Hoh come hon Sad Sack," said Princess, "hit's honly ha train. . ."

. . .but it wasn't an ordinary train. It was a GHOST TRAIN!
As soon as the Raggy Dolls climbed aboard there was a click, and a jerk, and the train moved off into the dark doorway!

As the train rattled and swerved through the darkness, the Raggy Dolls could hear horrible screams. They watched in horror as huge monsters appeared out of the gloom.

Suddenly, they were in daylight again, but where were they now? The Raggy Dolls staggered off the train and found a place to hide.

"I'm not sure I like it here," said Lucy, "it's full of scary things."

"Don't worry," said Back-to-Front, "that was just a ghost train, none of it was real!"

"I thought it was rather fun," admitted Dotty, "but this is no place for Dolls – let' go."

Just then, they heard Lord Stoneybroke's voice, very close to them.

"I say Bert, as soon as you've tested the big wheel, can you help me set up the firework display? I want to let it off as soon as it gets dark. That should bring the people in, eh what?"

"Very good m'lud," said Bert.

Suddenly the Raggy Dolls felt themselves being lifted up, up, up. . .they had hidden in one of the seats of the Big Wheel!

"Oh no," moaned Sad Sack, "whatever next?"

Soon they were going down, down, down. . .

"My tummy feels hall funny," groaned Princess.

Up and round and round and down they went until at last the big wheel stopped, with the Raggy Dolls stuck right at the very top!

"Oh why did we come?" whimpered Lucy.

Just then a pigeon landed on the hand-rail.

"Cooo," said the pigeon, "what are yooo doing up here?"

"We're stuck," explained Back-to-Front.

"Cooo," said the pigeon, "never mind, it's a lovely vieoooo!"

"Please can you help us?" begged Princess, who had no head for heights.

The pigeon agreed and flew the Raggy Dolls one by one to the top of the helter-skelter.

The Raggy Dolls thanked the pigeon and climbed on to a mat. "When we get to the bottom," said Dotty firmly, "we are definitely leaving!"

Down and down, and round and round they whooshed until at last they reached the bottom. Lot's of people had begun to arrive at the park!

"We must find somewhere to hide until it gets dark," said Back-to-Front.

Unfortunately, the nearest place was underneath the merry-go-round! It was VERY frightening when it suddenly started up, but the Raggy Dolls had to stay there until it was dark.

"Now's our chance," said Back-to-Front when the machinery stopped. The Raggy Dolls made good their escape while the people watched the firework display.

Safely back in the Reject Bin, the Raggy Dolls could at last begin to relax.

"Phew!" exclaimed Lucy, "I've had enough excitement to last me a year!"

"Mais oui," puffed Claude, "I am, 'ow you say, worn out!"

"Never again," vowed Sad Sack.

"Quite right," agreed Princess. "Hamusement Parks hought not to be hallowed!"

"Oh I don't know," said Back-to-Front cheerfully, "after all, they say life is full of little ups and downs." Everyone groaned except Dotty.

"We are NOT amused!" she said.